GW01018342

CÉSAR AUGUSTE FRANCK
25 SHORT PIECES from 'L'ORG

	Introduction	*page*	2
1	Song from the Creuse		3
2	Old Christmas Carol		4
3	Christmas Carol from Anjou		5
4	(Quasi andante)		6
5	(Andantino)		7
6	(Andantino quasi allegretto)		8
7	(Maestoso)		10
8	(Poco maestoso)		11
9	(Quasi lento)		12
10	(Poco lento)		13
11	Old Christmas Carol		14
12	(Andantino poco allegretto)		16
13	(Andante)		17
14	Christmas Carol from Anjou		18
15	(Poco allegretto)		19
16	(Allegretto vivo)		20
17	(Poco allegro)		22
18	(Allegretto)		23
19	Air from Béarn		24
20	Song from Béarn		25
21	(Maestoso)		26
22	(Non troppo lento)		27
23	Old Christmas Carol		28
24	(Poco allegro)		30
25	(Allegretto amabile)		32

ABRSM

Published by ABRSM (Publishing) Ltd, a wholly owned subsidiary of ABRSM
Printed in England by Halstan & Co. Ltd, Amersham, Bucks., on materials from sustainable sources
Reprinted in 2018

INTRODUCTION

César Franck (1822-1890) was born in Liège of Flemish stock. He started his music studies at Liège Conservatory with considerable acclaim, and at the age of 13 he moved with his family to Paris. He continued his studies at the Paris Conservatory, where he won many prizes for his composition, but it was not until late in life that he gained public recognition as a composer. For most of his lifetime he was better known as an organist (at the basilica of Ste Clotilde for over 30 years) and as a teacher (at the Jesuit College and the Paris Conservatory).

Although he wrote a number of vocal stage and sacred works, his finest composition achievement is represented by the symphonic, chamber and keyboard works: particularly the Symphony in D minor, the Symphonic Variations for piano and orchestra, a sonata for violin and piano, a string quartet and a piano quintet.

Among his last compositions were a collection of pieces for the harmonium, intended for use by church organists and published posthumously by Enoch of Paris. His original plan encompassed 91 pieces but only 59 had been completed when he died as the result of a street accident. These miniatures, although written for the harmonium, sound just as pleasing on the piano where their harmonic originality can perhaps be better appreciated.

Twenty-five of these pieces have been selected for this edition. The original edition has been followed, and editorial interpolations are shown either within square brackets or, in the case of slurs and ties, by a vertical stroke. The metronome mark at the end of each piece is only a suggestion and should not be regarded as authoritative.

Song from the Creuse

FRANCK

4

Old Christmas Carol

The melody can be played an octave higher, if desired.

Christmas Carol from Anjou

6

8

Andantino quasi allegretto

poco rall.

a tempo

molto dolce

rall.

[♩ = c. 108]

10

Poco maestoso

8

[♩ = c. 96]

12

Old Christmas Carol

Andantino poco allegretto

12

[♩ = c. 116]

Christmas Carol from Anjou

AB 1881

Poco allegro

17

$[\mathbf{\downarrow} = c. 138]$

Allegretto

Air from Béarn

$[\quad = c. 112]$

Song from Béarn

Poco allegretto

20

[p] dolce

[legato]

pp

[p] dolce

rall.

pp

1) D♭ in original.
Grace-notes should be played on the beat.

AB 1881

[♩ = c. 112]

Old Christmas Carol

Allegretto amabile

25

1) B♭ in the original.

[♩ = c. 126]